Hans-Günter Heumann

Piano Junior

A Creative and Interactive Piano Course for Children
Duet Book 4

ED 13824

Illustrations by Leopé

SCHOTT

Mainz · London · Berlin · Madrid · New York · Paris · Prague · Tokyo · Toronto
© 2018 SCHOTT MUSIC Ltd. London. Printed in Germany

ED 13824
British Library Cataloguing-in-Publication-Data.
A catalogue record for this book is available from the British Library.
ISMN 979-0-2201-3652-8
UPC 841 8860 26711

Cover illustration by Leopé (www.leope.com)
Cover photography: iStockphoto
Cover design: www.adamhaystudio.com
Audio tracks recorded, mixed and mastered by:
Last Eigth Recording Studio, London
Audio tracks performed by Samantha Ward and Maciej Raginia
Printed in Germany S&Co.9215

Contents

Please visit **www.piano-junior.com** to stream or download demo and play-along recordings for all the tunes in the book.

Secondo

1. Mother's Song

Op. 99, No. 2

Moderato ♩ = 120

Alexander Gretchaninov (1864–1956)

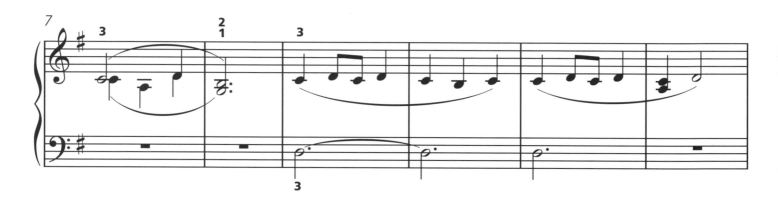

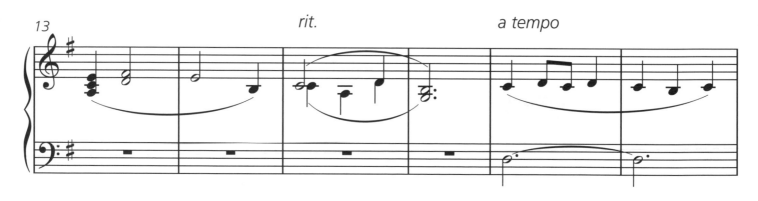

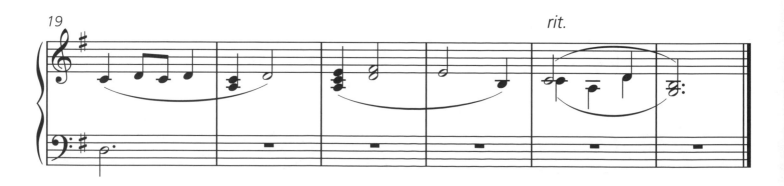

1. Mother's Song

Op. 99, No. 2

Alexander Gretchaninov (1864–1956)

Moderato ♩ = 120

mf cantando

rit.

a tempo *

rit.

*) Return to the previous tempo

Alexander Gretchaninov was a Russian composer. His works include piano pieces and operas especially for children. He had a particular gift for creating simple, melodic and expressive music.

2. Island in the Sun

HGH

6

2. Island in the Sun

HGH

3. Greensleeves

English Folk Song
Arr.: HGH

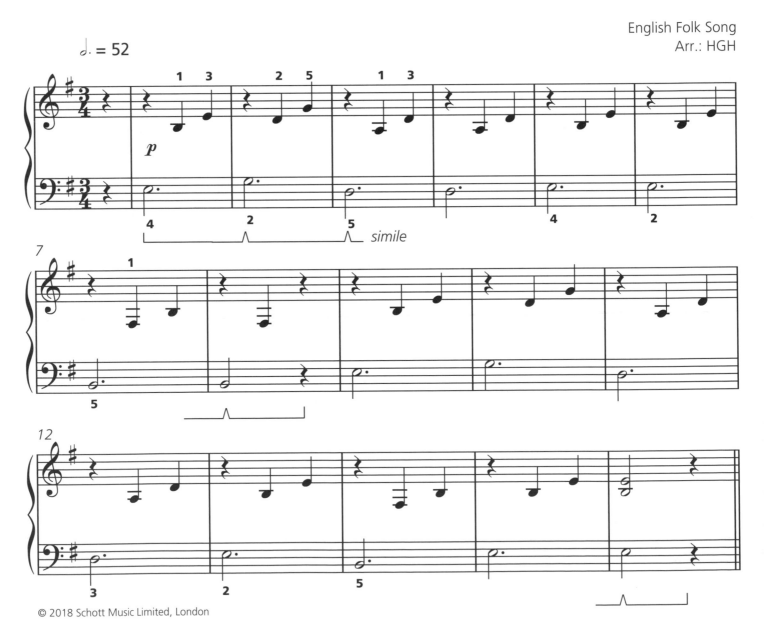

3. Greensleeves

English Folk Song
Arr.: HGH

A - las, my love,___ you do me wrong___ to cast me off___ dis-

cour - teous - ly, and I have loved___ you so

long___ de - light - ing in___ your com - pa - ny.

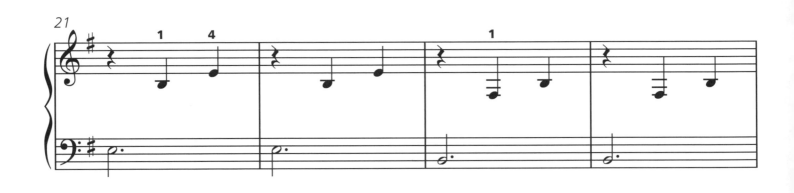

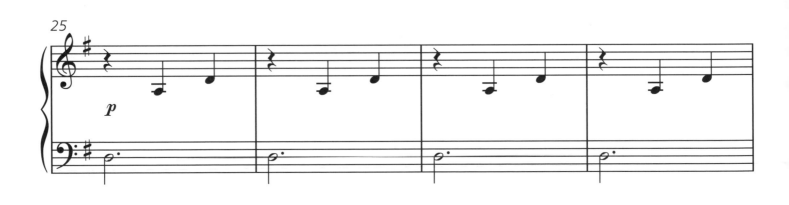

Green - - sleeves_____ was all my joy,_____

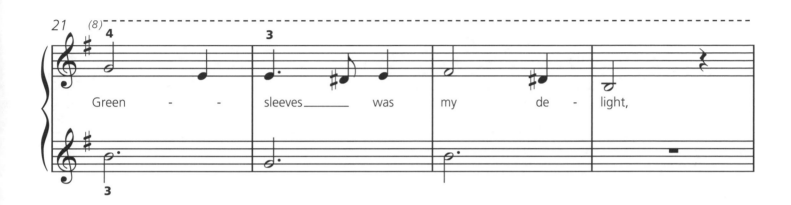

Green - - sleeves_____ was my de - light,

Green - - sleeves was my heart of gold,_____ and

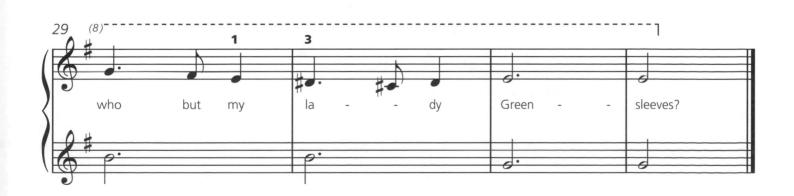

who but my la - - dy Green - - sleeves?

4. Allegro

Op. 149, No. 13

Anton Diabelli (1781–1858)

4. Allegro

Op. 149, No. 13

♩ = 132

Anton Diabelli (1781–1858)

13

5. The Happy Farmer

from *Album for the Young*, Op. 68, No. 10

Robert Schumann (1810–1856)
Arr.: Theodor Kirchner (1823–1903)

5. The Happy Farmer

from *Album for the Young*, Op. 68, No. 10

Robert Schumann (1810–1856)
Arr.: Theodor Kirchner (1823–1903)

Robert Schumann was a German composer, pianist, critic and essayist - and husband of the pianist Clara Schumann. In piano lessons his works *Album for the Young Op. 68* and *Scenes from Childhood Op. 15* are particularly popular.

15

6. Bella ciao

Italian Folk Song
Arr.: HGH

6. Bella ciao

Italian Folk Song
Arr.: HGH

7. Mexican Hat Dance

Jarabe Tapatio

Mexican Folk Song
Arr.: HGH

7. Mexican Hat Dance

Jarabe Tapatio

Mexican Folk Song
Arr.: HGH

D. C. al Fine with repetition

8. Down by the Riverside

Spiritual
Arr.: HGH

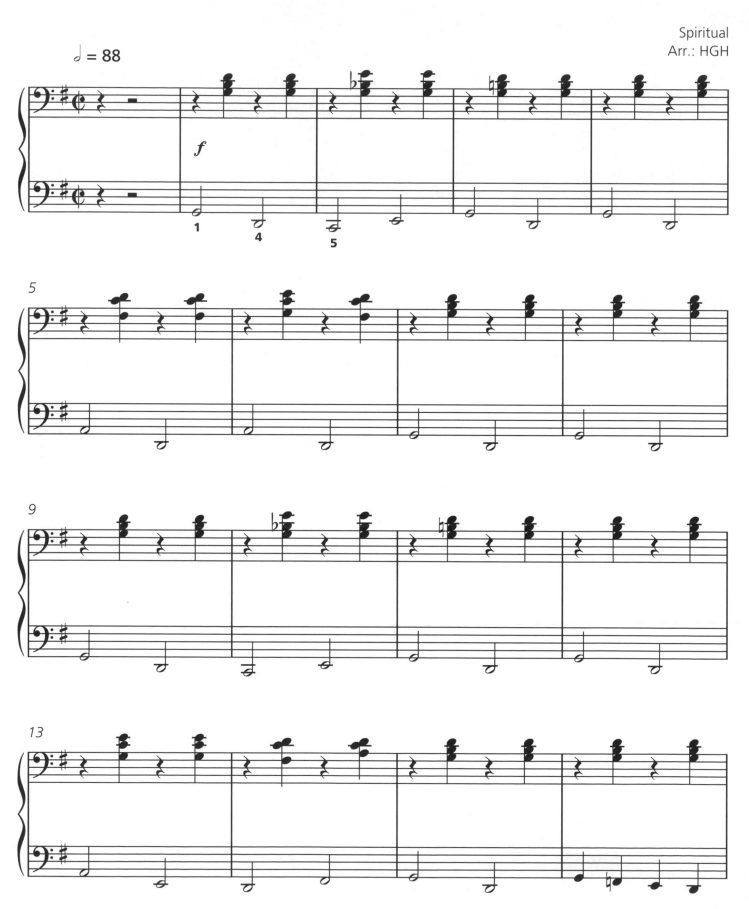

8. Down by the Riverside

Spiritual
Arr.: HGH

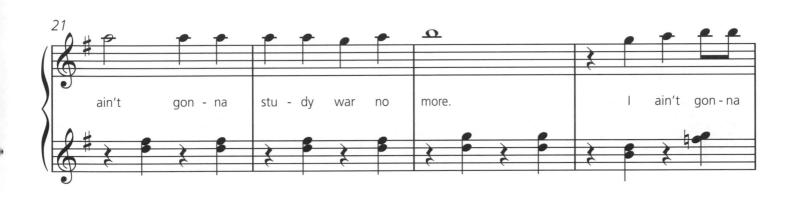

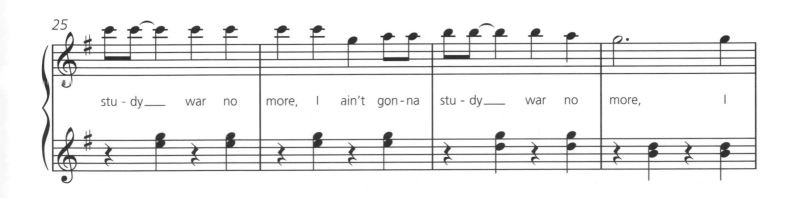

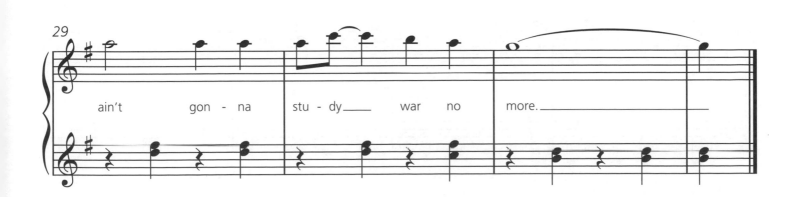

23

9. Fips in the Park*

Mike Schoenmehl (*1957)

*) Fips = name of a monkey

9. Fips in the Park*

Mike Schoenmehl (*1957)

*) Fips = name of a monkey

*) to be played less, for example: meno forte = less loud

10. Serious Song

Largo ♩ = 60

Daniel Gottlob Türk (1750–1813)

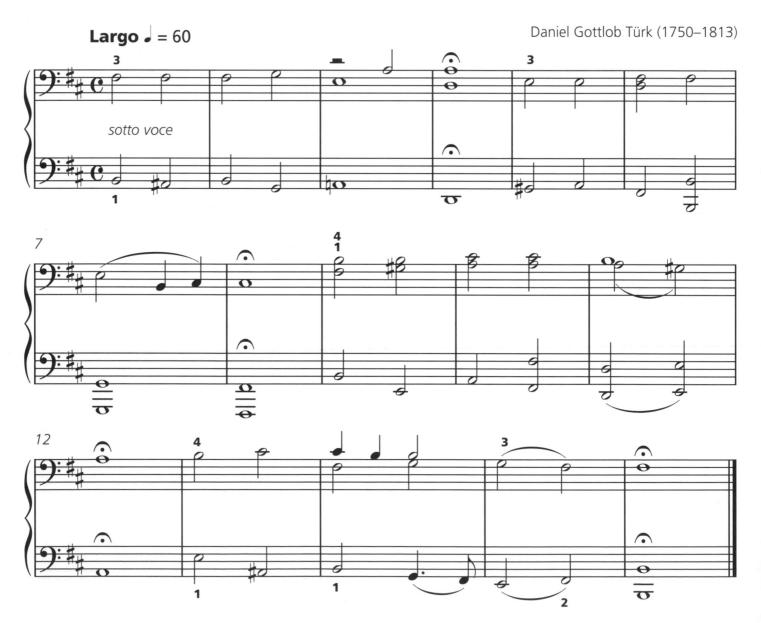

sotto voce

10. Serious Song

Daniel Gottlob Türk (1750–1813)

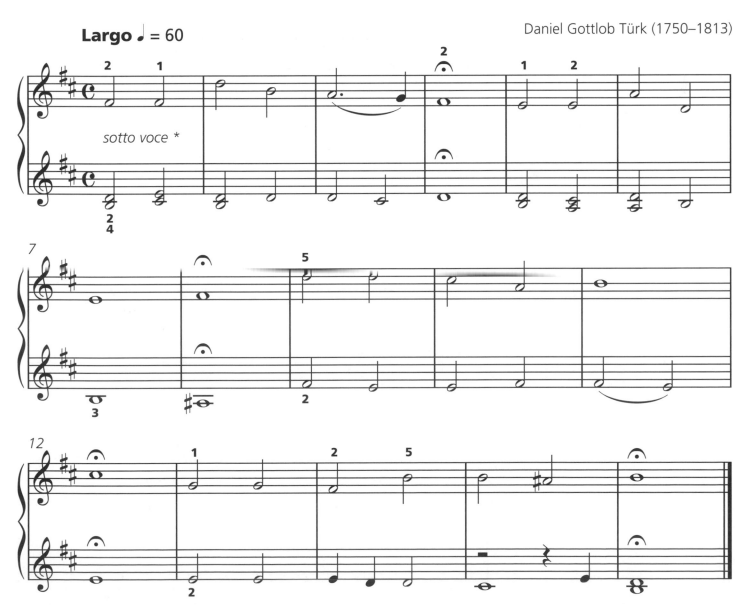

*sotto voce *

*) sotto voce (Ital.: under the voice) is a lowering of the vocal or instrumental volume

11. German Dance

K 606, No. 5

Wolfgang Amadeus Mozart (1756–1791)

11. German Dance

K 606, No. 5

Wolfgang Amadeus Mozart (1756–1791)

12. Sleeping Giant

Jürgen Moser (*1949)

32

12. Sleeping Giant

Jürgen Moser (*1949)

from: J. Moser, Just for fun, Groovy Piano Duets, Schott ED 8575

13. Hongroise

Op. 149, No. 20

♩ = 92

Anton Diabelli (1781–1858)

13. Hongroise

Op. 149, No. 20

Anton Diabelli (1781–1858)

14. In a Funny Mood

Eduard Pütz (1911–2000)

14. In a Funny Mood

With humour ♩ = 116

Eduard Pütz (1911–2000)

from: E. Pütz, *Let's play together, 10 jazzy pieces for piano duet*, Schott ED 8482

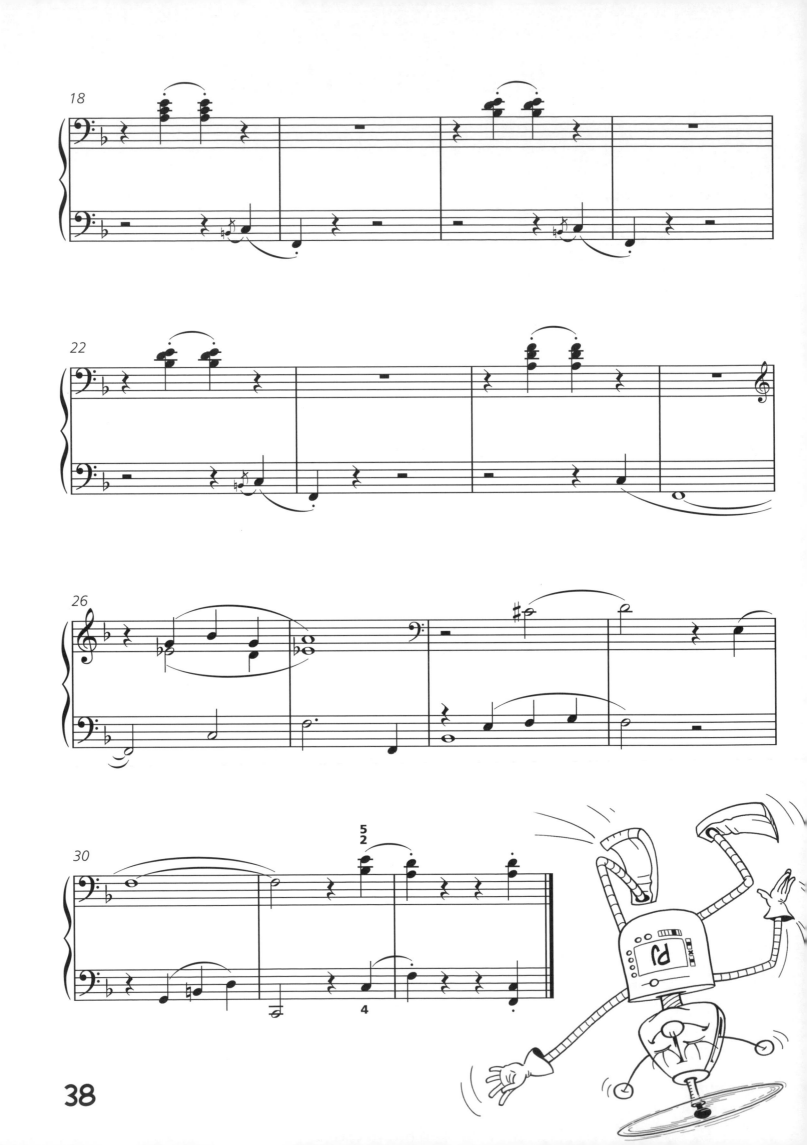